DORIS VAN LIEW FOSTER

# *Feather in the Wind*

## THE STORY OF A HURRICANE

## *Illustrated by Ati Forberg*

# *Lothrop, Lee & Shepard Co. / New York*

Text copyright © 1972 by Doris Van Liew Foster / Illustrations copyright © 1972 by Ati Forberg
Inquiries should be addressed to Lothrop, Lee and Shepard Company, 105 Madison Ave., New York, N. Y. 10016 / Printed in the United States of America / Library of Congress Catalog Card Number: 75-171616

To Stephen

Telltale signs warned of a storm.
The sun had turned away.
The sky was muddy yellow—
a strange sky color.
The palm trees stood stiff and silent.
It was the stillness
that was most foreboding.

But before long,
sudden whirls of wind
and spurts of rain broke the silence.

Small creatures sought a hideaway,
some beneath twisted roots and vines,
others squeezed into pockets of coral.
A squirrel ran to a hole in a tree;
birds flew into thick shrubbery.

A gust of wind known as a windflaw
carried an old land crab miles from his home,
to shove him close to a fence.
There he huddled, quite safe, in the long grass.

The storm that threatened from a distance
traveled slowly.
It became bigger and bigger.
Its bulging sides stretched for miles.
Sometimes it stood resting, catching its breath.

The storm meandered westward.
Then, following a current of air, it turned east.
Its winds increased until it was no longer a
tropical storm, but a full-blown hurricane.

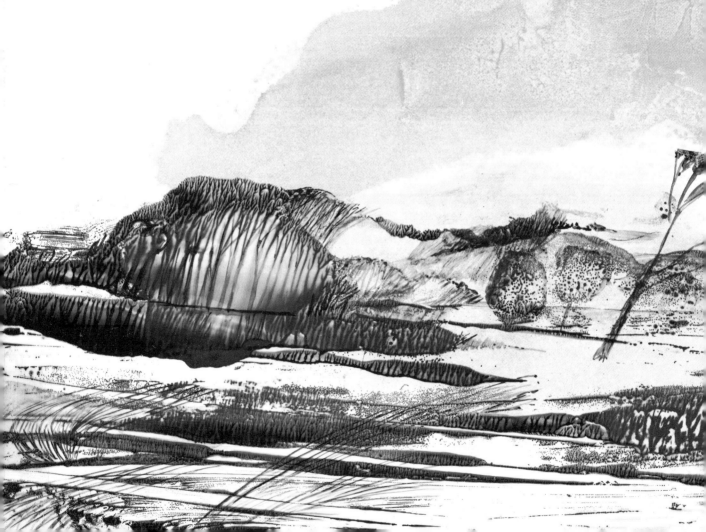

Like all hurricanes, it was given a girl's name . . .
Hortense.

The weatherman knew Hortense well—
how strong her winds were
and what course she was taking.
His forecast was:
"Hortense is headed this way.
She has picked up speed over the water.
Unless she changes course, she will strike today.
Stay tuned for weather bulletins."

Stephen helped his father storm-shutter the windows.
Small things—a birdfeeder, a swing—
they stored indoors.

"Why do we have hurricanes?" Stephen asked.

His father thought about it.
"In August and September, when the ocean
is warm from being in the sun all summer, it heats
the air above it.
This warm air is lighter than the air around it,
so it begins to rise—the way bubbles do in a pot of
boiling water.

"As the bubbles of air rise, they get bigger, because the higher they go, the less pressure there is. They get colder too—cold enough to make the water vapor in the air condense into water droplets.

"When water vapor condenses, heat is left over. The heat raises the bubbles until they build up the towering cumulus clouds that form a thunderstorm."

"But a hurricane isn't a thunderstorm,"
Stephen interrupted.

"No," his father said. "But thunderstorms release a lot of energy. Sometimes—and not even scientists know just how—several thunderstorms get together. Each storm releases energy to keep the others going, and a hurricane is formed.

"The winds in the wall of a hurricane travel as fast as 200 miles an hour; yet 30 miles away, the center of the storm is calm. We call this quiet center the eye.

"All that warm, moist air I told you about spirals in toward the eye of the storm. The closer to the center it gets, the faster it spins. A hurricane is a big cone of whirling air, spiraling upward like smoke rising through a chimney."

"How do hurricanes get to us?" Stephen asked.

"Well," his father said. "A hurricane starts near the
equator, where the water is the warmest. Then
it's carried along by currents of air, the way a boat is
carried along a stream. In our part of the country,
these air currents flow mainly toward our east coast."

All this while Hortense was coming closer.
Now sheets of rain began to whip at the
boarded-up buildings, to tear across empty streets.
The heads of palm trees bent low,
spinning faster and faster
until they looked like bunches of torn rags.

Gradually hidden by the rain,
the sky could no longer be seen.

A hurricane has a sound, a beat,
like no other wind.
That sound was beginning now—
BOOM, SWISH—BOOM, SWISH

Strangely enough,
a hurricane sometimes brings gifts.
This one did.

From the depths of the sea
Hortense dug shells of various colors and shapes
and lavished them on the beach.

Slamming inland, she paused,
unpredictable as ever.
From the air she snatched something
so small that it slipped from her grasp.
It fell to the ground near Stephen's house.
In spite of the blurring rain outside the window,
he spied it there and ran outside.

A handful of tangled feathers,
the bird was limp in his hand.
Stephen held it close to him
and ran back indoors,
struggling to close the door against
the hurricane's fury.

Stephen showed the bird to his father.
"I wish it could open its eyes.
It looks half dead."

"Perhaps you were in time to save the bird,"
his father said,
"but it needs to be kept warm and dry."

While Stephen searched his room
for something to put the bird in, he thought,
"If I got lost in a storm,
I'd want someone to find me and keep me warm."

At last he found a box the right size.
His old sweater would make a soft lining for it.

"Little bird, this shoebox will be your bed."
Gently he laid the bird inside.

Meanwhile, the weatherman warned:
"The winds are reaching their peak.
Stay indoors.
Only those who must should venture out.
Your weather service will keep you advised
of any change.
Stay tuned to this station."

Hortense was wild, a noisy terror.
The earth became her plaything—
to wash, to squeeze,
to rip apart, to whirl in her arms
at unbelievable speed.

Small creatures and things
left unprotected fell victim
to her fierce winds.

Stephen's bird woke up and gave a feeble cry.
Stephen tried to give it food,
but the bird refused to open its bill.
Turning its head feebly from side to side,
it looked around, then back at Stephen.

Stephen's father had been watching
and now he said,
"Perhaps your bird is not asking
for food but calling for its mother.
Remember, it's been torn from its home
and beaten by the storm."

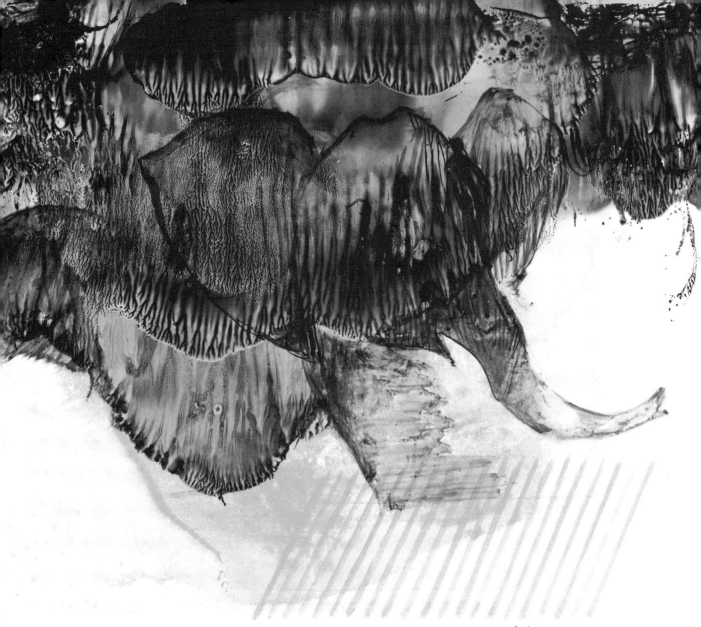

The bird continued to cry out as Hortense blew.
All afternoon she blew, and far into the night
she kept the moon and the stars out of sight.

Small creatures stayed hidden.
Stephen covered the bird for the night.

In his bed Stephen listened to the wind.
"The hurricane sounds like a big elephant
that is caught in a fence," he thought.
"I can hear her *swish, swish* with her trunk
and *pound, pound* with her feet,
fighting, fighting to be free.
*Swish, swish. Pound, pound.*
*Swish, swish. Pound, pound.*

"People cannot help her
or stop her or turn her around,
that old hurricane elephant,
going *swissh, swisssh, pounnd, pounnnnd.*"

Stephen fell asleep.

In the morning
the weatherman reported:
"Hortense is no longer a danger.
She has moved out to sea,
and during the night
her winds diminished so that
she can barely be called a hurricane now.

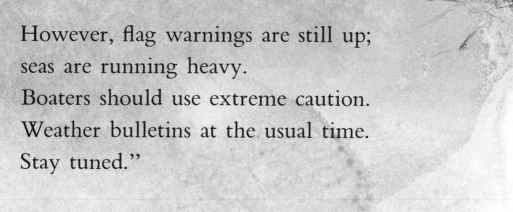

However, flag warnings are still up;
seas are running heavy.
Boaters should use extreme caution.
Weather bulletins at the usual time.
Stay tuned."

Once again a blue sky framed the face of the sun.
Palm trees fanned themselves dry.
A squirrel somersaulted in the mango tree.
Sparrows flew in happy company.
Old land crab, plainly out of place,
loomed white and ghostlike
as he sidled along the fence.

People came out into the sunshine,
curious to see what damage Hortense had done.
They found streets blocked by fallen trees,
power poles and lines down,
and coconuts by the hundreds on the ground.

Stephen and his father brought the bird outside.

Could this jaunty little fellow be that wet
bedraggled thing rescued from the storm?

The bird's feathers had dried to a soft blue-jay blue.
Down from his cap ran a ribbon of black,
framing his darting eyes and long pointed beak.
His round body ended in a stubby tail,
giving him a chopped-off look, quite comical.

When Stephen put him down, he hopped over the
ground screaming, *"Squweeee, squweeee, squweeee!"*

Stephen and his father waited anxiously.
Would the mother bird hear her young jay?

The answer soon came.
A large jay swooped down, rustling its
feathers, and screaming.

Then several more circled in,
and the young jay and his mother were engulfed
by excited, milling birds.

Now that the young jay was in his mother's care,
Stephen's father said,
"Let's walk along the beach."

The waves were riding high;
the gulls were screaming and wheeling in the sky.
Stephen idly picked up shells,
then tossed them away until he found one he liked.
"Look at this shell," he cried.
"It curves like the wing of a bird."
He turned the shell slowly in his hands,
tracing with his finger the veins of color.

"I am going to keep this forever."